Encyclopedia Brown's
First Book of
Puzzles and Games

HEY, KIDS!

Do you have a wacky story to tell about an animal, a fact, a crime, a sport? The funnier and wackier the better! But it must be *true*.

You can write about it, or enclose a clipping from your local newspaper, or send a note from your parents or teacher verifying the story. If it is included in an Encyclopedia Brown book, your name will appear in the book.

Send your wacky true story (along with your name and address) to: Encyclopedia Brown, c/o Bantam Books, 666 Fifth Avenue, New York 10103.

Encyclopedia Brown's
First Book of Puzzles and Games

BY JIM RAZZI

Based upon the Encyclopedia Brown Series
created by Donald J. Sobol

A BANTAM SKYLARK BOOK

ENCYCLOPEDIA BROWN'S FIRST BOOK
OF PUZZLES AND GAMES

*A Bantam Book / published by arrangement with
Elsevier/Nelson Books*

*Bantam Skylark edition / February 1980
2nd printing .... September 1980*

ISBN 0-553-15300-5

Published simultaneously in the United States and Canada

PRINTED IN THE UNITED STATES OF AMERICA

11 10 9 8 7 6 5 4 3

Introduction

Here's Encyclopedia and all the gang in their first *Puzzles and Games Book*. Now you can have more fun with America's Sherlock Holmes in sneakers.

There are clues to spot, codes to crack, mazes to solve, word games, picture puzzles and lots more! It's all here, so grab a pencil and your wits for hours of stimulating, brain-teasing fun!

Crime Wave

It's a sleepy day in Idaville but even so, Encyc-lopedia Brown has observed four crimes taking place. Can you spot them?

The Line Up

Chief Brown, Encyclopedia's father, has just caught Spider Spinoza, the jewel thief. He's in the line-up on the next page. A detective had been trailing him all day and gave this report to Chief Brown:

"I first observed Spider Spinoza in a drugstore, buying a comb. I knew that he was probably up to no good, so I followed him. After the drugstore, he went to an eye doctor to have his eyeglasses cleaned. He left the eye doctor and walked down 3rd Street. It started to rain just then and Spider opened his umbrella. I then observed him going into a jewelry store. While in the jewelry store, he stole a number of items while the owner was busy with another customer. He put these items in his jacket pocket and ran out of the store. It was then that I identified myself as a policeman and nabbed him."

Now that you know the detective's report, tell us who is Spider Spinoza, A, B, C, D or E?

A B C D E

Match the Prints

Encyclopedia Brown is trying to match up some fingerprints. See if you can help. In the fingerprints below, only two are exactly alike. Which are they?

1.   2.   3.   4.

5.   6.   7.   8.

Encyclopedia meets The Brain

Brains Malloy was the brainiest kid in Idaville next to Encyclopedia. Some say that it was even. So to settle the question, Brains sent a message to Encyclopedia. The message explained itself and after a few hard looks, Encyclopedia got it. Can you? Here is the message that Brains sent.

$$\frac{\text{STAND}}{\text{I}} \text{ THAT YOU } \frac{\text{NEVER}}{\text{LOOK}} \text{ A CLUE.}$$

$$\text{IF } \frac{\text{STAND}}{\text{YOU CAN}} \text{ THIS MESSAGE, I WILL}$$

BELIEVE THAT AND ADMIT YOU ARE SMARTER THAN I AM.

BRAINS MALLOY

Prehistoric Word Find

In *The Case of the Cave Drawings,* a dishonest teenager tries to cash in on phony prehistoric paintings. But Encyclopedia spots the fake when he realizes that dinosaurs and cavemen don't mix. In the word find below, however, we did mix cavemen and dinosaurs. They're all hidden, of course, so you'll have to find them. You can go forward, backward, vertically, horizontally and diagonally. Draw a pencil line around each word as you find it. Look for: LIZARD, PREHISTORIC, CLUB, DINOSAUR, VOLCANO, EARTHQUAKE, SPEAR, FIRE, SUN, CAVEMAN, MAMMAL and ROC (a legendary giant bird).

```
E A R T H A R I F L O P
R V O L A C O R L I R P
U O D S A E U A A Z R R
O L U V C A V E M A N E
S P E R S R O P M R I H
O M T O L T L S A D D I
N A N C A H C I M C R S
I I L O M Q A H L H R T
D U N M S U N E T A A O
B I A A E A O I A R Z R
D M U R A K A P I I I I
S O N I M E V A C F L C
```

Clue Code

Here's one of Encyclopedia's "Clue Codes." He's
sure that none of the Tigers would be smart
enough to get the message if they ever found it.

Here is how it works:
☐ stands for a consonant (T,N,C,S etc.)
☆ stands for a vowel (A,E,I etc.)
Now from the clues, guess the words and then
read the message downward.

$$\begin{array}{rll}
☐☆☆☐ = & \text{(To come together)} & = \underline{\hspace{4cm}} \\
☐☆ = & \text{(Meaning myself)} & = \underline{\hspace{4cm}} \\
☆☐ = & \text{(Inside)} & = \underline{\hspace{4cm}} \\
☐☐☆ = & \text{(Definite article)} & = \underline{\hspace{4cm}} \\
☆☐☐ = & \text{(Not young)} & = \underline{\hspace{4cm}} \\
☐☆☐☐ = & \text{(A farm building)} & = \underline{\hspace{4cm}} \\
☐☆☐☆☐☐☐ = & \text{(This evening)} & = \underline{\hspace{4cm}}
\end{array}$$

Sea Monster

In *The Case of the Red Boat,* Encyclopedia and his father go out fishing and end up netting a pair of thieves.

They were lucky they didn't meet up with this monster while on the water. Which monster? Well, it's an eight-armed creature of the deep. If you can guess its name, put it on the dashed lines below. Now take a pencil and shade in all the areas below that have the letters that make up that name. __ __ __ __ __ __ __

Short Cut Maze

Encyclopedia wants to take a short cut to his home across the fenced-in backyards. See if you can find the shortest route to his home. Begin at START and find your way to HOME. You cannot cross any lines. Here's a hint: The shortest way will pass by only four houses.

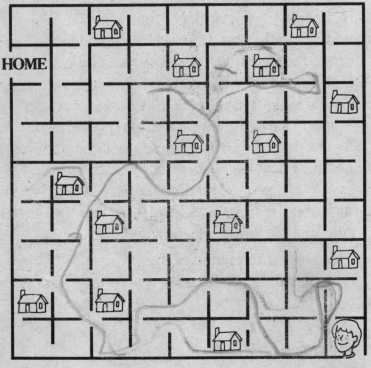

HOME

START

15

Spot the Clue

A jewelry store has been robbed and Chief Brown and Encyclopedia hurry to the scene. When they get there, a store clerk explains what happened. He was there alone, he says, because the owner had gone out to lunch. Suddenly, he continued, while he was in the back of the store, someone outside threw a brick through the window. The window breaker reached in and grabbed some rings, necklaces and watches. While he was doing this, he dropped his cap. He then ran down the street and disappeared. The clerk said that he had telephoned Chief Brown immediately. He also said that he had left everything exactly as it was because he knew that the police would want it that way. Chief Brown nodded and then he and Encyclopedia looked over the scene. Encyclopedia spotted something right away that told him that the clerk was lying. Can you spot the clue that Encyclopedia saw?

A picture of the scene of the crime is on the next page.

Bugs Bugs Brown

Bugs Meany, who was always trying to bug Encyclopedia Brown and get even with him, made up these trick stories. In each story, there is one mistake. Bugs told the stories to Encyclopedia Brown in front of a group of kids, hoping that Encyclopedia would make a fool of himself. Encyclopedia of course found the mistake in each story. Can you? Here are the stories:

Late Lucy Washburn lived in a lovely, one-leveled ranch-style house on Elm Street. They called her Late Lucy because she was never on time for anything. One day, she had a date to go skate boarding with Ruth Phillips at three o'clock that afternoon. She had some chores to take care of first, however, and before she knew it, it was ten minutes to three and she wasn't ready yet. Lucy made up her mind not to be late this time, though. She rushed around as if she were doing the latest dance, the hop, skip and jump, and was finished just as Punctual Phillips rang the doorbell. Lucy ran down the stairs and opened the door. It was exactly three o'clock. Lucy was all out of breath but she had made it on time for once!

*

Mario Piccolo was the star catcher of the Idaville Little League baseball team. The team had worked out all day and Mario was dog-tired when he returned home that night. He decided to turn in early and get a lot of sleep. The next day was the big game with the Baystown Bashers and Mario wanted to be good and rested. So at nine o'clock that night, he went up to his bedroom, laid his mitt on his bedside table, and quickly put on his pajamas. He set the alarm on his big alarm clock to go off at nine-thirty the next morning. The alarm always woke him up. No sooner had his head hit the pillow then he was fast asleep. At fifteen minutes past nine, a car's horn honked loudly outside Mario's window but he didn't hear a thing. The next thing he knew it was nine-thirty, the alarm was ringing and the sun was shining. Mario picked up his cat-cher's mitt from the table and thought about the coming game. It was going to be tough, but he was sure they would win.

Name the Case

A mis-typed note gave Encyclopedia the answer to this sparkling gem of a case. To find out which case it was, solve the acrostic puzzle.

Here is what to do: Guess the words from the clues, and write the letters in the spaces above the numbers. Then transfer the letters to the same numbered boxes in the grid on the next page. You will then find the name of the case.

1. Bugs Meany is a __ __ __ __ __ member
              1 21 19 3 20

2. Opposite of fat __ __ __ __
           10 2 14 18

3. Another word for enemy __ __ __
               9 8 7

4. His Majesty's Ship __ __ __
         11 13 15

5. Encyclopedia hung this outside his garage. __ __ __ __
        6 17 23 22

6. What Encyclopedia loved to work on __ __ __ __
        4 5 16 12

1	2	3	4	5	6	7	8	9	10	11	12
13	14	15	16	17	18	19	20	21	22	23	

The Case of the Busy Chief

Chief Brown had to go to various places on his way home from the Idaville Police Station. He was a busy man so he asked his son, Encyclopedia, to find out the best way he could go to all the places. Encyclopedia solved the problem by drawing a map of the roads that led to all the places. He then traced a route on the roads with a pencil that passed through each place. He never passed the the same place twice, however, and he never went back over his line. Can you do it?

Begin at START and end at FINISH.

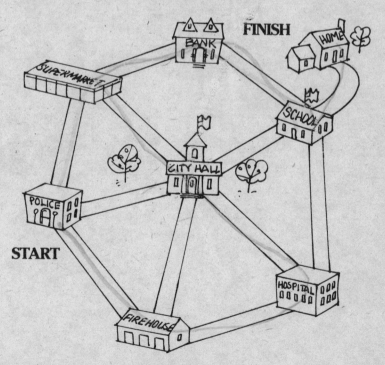

What's in a Name?

Billy Stein was a very scientific kid. So it was no surprise when he came into Encyclopedia's garage one summer morning and said: "I would like to hire you to find my pet *eight-legged wingless arachnid.* I've lost it and it was more fun than a barrel of *simians.* I used to have *a warm-blooded vertebrate covered with feathers* but it died. I then owned a *mammal with leathery wings* but it slept a lot in the daytime, so I gave it away. I then bought a *scaly, limbless long-bodied reptile* but it became lost in the grass. Before I lost my latest pet, I had an *aquatic and land mollusk with a spiral shell* but it was too boring to play with. Do you think you can find my pet?

Encyclopedia said that he would give it a try. Sally Kimball just looked at Encyclopedia Brown with her mouth open.

"Do you know what he was talking about?" she asked in wonder. "Sure," answered Encyclopedia, "Don't you?"

If you know the animals that are italicized above. write them in order below.

1._____   3._____   5._____

2._____   4._____   6._____

P. S. If you don't know the animals, look up the answers and then have fun trying them out on your friends.

Movie Crossword

In *The Case of the Missing Statue,* Chief Brown and Encyclopedia try to help a movie star. But it seemed that her problem was just a big act to get attention. Pay attention to this movie crossword and see if you can solve it and be in the spotlight.

ACROSS

1. Movie city
7. North America (abbr.)
8. Murder movie
9. Mother
12. Travolta or Redford
15. Movie monster
16. Famous actors and actresses
18. Slim
21. Setting of movie or play
22. Nickel (symbol)
23. Cinemascope is seen on what? (2 wds.)

DOWN

2. Not young
3. Shoot-'em-up movie
4. Before two
5. Betcha can't do it!
6. Cougar
10. Sophia Loren or Suzanne Somers
11. Twelve o'clock
13. Sherlock Holmes or Inspector Clouseau
14. Outdoor movie
17. Movie film wheels
19. Baseball team (how many?)
20. Batman sound

Pinball Wizard

Tilt Wilson is the pinball champ of Idaville. He has a high score of 140 points. One day, Sally Kimball challenged him to a game and beat him! See if you can beat Tilt's high score of 140 yourself.

Here is how to play:

Start at the STAR, and with a light pencil line, find your way to the FINISH. When you pass through a numbered opening add that number to your score. You cannot cross over your own line and you can't go through the same opening twice otherwise, TILT!

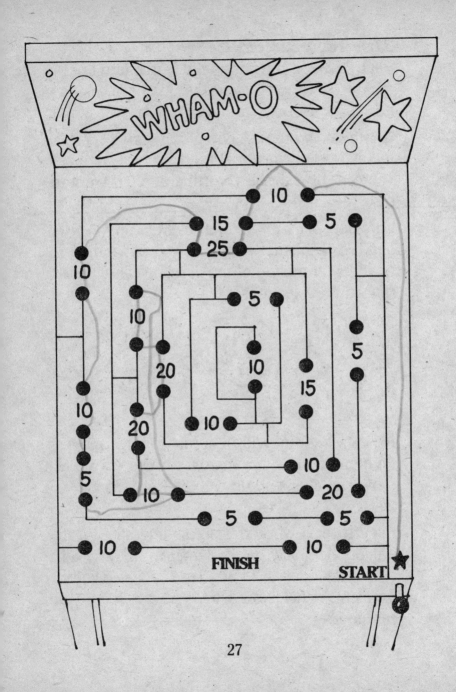

The Two-Bit Mystery

Benny Parker, the puzzle nut, came into Encyclopedia Brown's Detective Agency shaking his head. Encyclopedia asked him what was wrong.

"It's this coin puzzle," Benny answered, "I can't make head nor tail of it! It's driving me crazy. If you can solve this, it's worth a quarter. Want the case?"

Encyclopedia said yes and asked Benny to tell him the problem. Benny plunked down three quarters on the top of the gasoline can and arranged them like this:

1.   2.   3.

He then told Encyclopedia that in three moves, no more, no less, turning over two coins at each move, he must end up with all heads facing upward.

Encyclopedia worked his brain overtime for this one but he finally got it. Benny went away a happy puzzle-lover and Encyclopedia was twenty-five cents richer. Now why don't you see if you can do it?

Letter-Wise

Sally Kimball, Encyclopedia's partner, wrote down these letters on a slip of paper. Each letter stands for the name of something and there is a natural sequence to them. There is one last letter missing. Can you tell us what it is? Here are the letters:

M T W T F S ?

If you got that one, try this next one that Encyclopedia Brown wrote down. Each letter below represents a number: Can you tell us what the next letter should be?

O T T F F S S ?

Crazy Graffiti

The latest party game in Idaville is crazy graffiti. The idea is to figure out what the words really stand for. It can be the name of a famous person, an object or a common saying. For instance, number 3 stands for "double time." Now try to guess the rest.

1. RAIN

2. CLASS

3. TIME TIME

4. FOOT

5. DOG

6. HIGH

7. SUN

8. MOON

9. MOUNTAIN

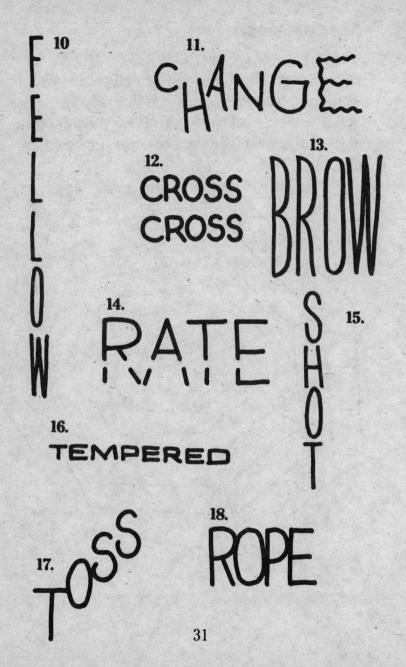

10. FELLOW

11. CHANGE

12. CROSS CROSS

13. BROW

14. RATE RATE

15. SHOT

16. TEMPERED

17. TOSS

18. ROPE

31

Spider Maze

In *The Case of the Whistling Ghost,* an unbroken spider's web was the clue to catch a camera thief. This web, however, *is* broken but only in spots. See if you can get from A to B by staying on the lines of the web. You cannot cross a break in a line.

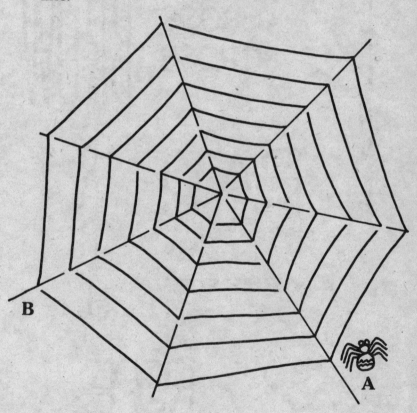

B

A

A Visual Trick

Roscoe Kippers is Idaville's amateur kid magician. He likes to come up with optical illusions to show his friends. Here's one that he just came up with.

What to do:

There is a hidden message in the jumble of lines below. To see it, just hold the page at an angle away from you and close one eye. Look in the direction of the arrow, beginning at START and move around clockwise. Can you see the message?

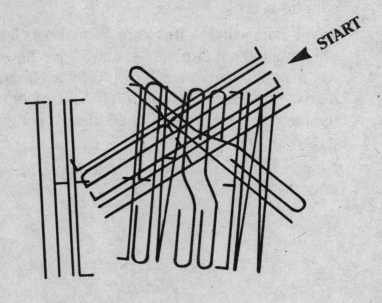

A Short Mystery

See if you can solve a mystery just like Encyclopedia Brown would.

Here is the mystery:

A short man was in an empty room. There was a cloth bag hanging from a hook near the ceiling. The short man had money hidden in the bag. He was much too short to reach the bag by himself and there was absolutely no other furniture or manmade object in the room. Yet the man reached up slowly and took the bag off the hook with his hand.

Below is a picture of the scene a few hours later. The man did not remove anything from the room in that time. It is still empty. In fact, there is a great, big puddle of water on the floor which the man can't clean up because there is not even a mop around.

Now tell us. How did he get his money bag down?

Witness to the Crime

Encyclopedia Brown was just coming out of the Beefy Burger Palace when he witnessed this bank robbery. He carefully noted a number of things as a good witness should. Later, when his father, Chief Brown, asked him some questions, Encyclopedia was ready with the answers.

Now see if you can do the same. Study the picture of the robbery below and try to remember all the details. Then turn the page and answer the questions. Don't peek back.

1. How many robbers were there? *2*

2. What was the license number of
   the getaway car? *3599*

3. What time did the robbery take place? *3:00*

4. What was the name of the bank that
   was robbed? *1st n @ bqnk*

5. At what avenue and street was the
   getaway car parked? *a Holly*

6. The robber getting into the car:
   A. Was he masked? *yes*
   B. Did he wear a hat? *yes*
   C. Was his shirt striped or checked? *no*
   D. Did he wear sunglasses? *no*
   E. Was he armed? *yes*

7. What's the address of the bank? *960 Holly*

Cryptograms

One of Encyclopedia Brown's favorite pastimes is solving cryptograms. A cryptogram is a code in which other letters are substituted for the real letters of the alphabet. Now, of course, in any one cryptogram, you don't know yet which letters stand for the real letters. You have to figure it out a little at a time by trial and error. It's not as hard as it sounds. For instance, a single letter standing alone will usually stand for I or A. A group of three letters occurring frequently throughout the cryptogram, will usually be AND or THE. These are used frequently in sentences. Two letters together will probably be AS, DO, IS, IT, OF and so on.

As you start getting some letters, you will then get parts of words. Then you can guess what the rest of the letters are. For example, if you figured out that G I O K I L stood for D O C T O ? so far; you can guess that the last L will stand for R and the word would be D O C T O R. Now of course you know that all the other L's in the cryptogram stand for R also. You also know that all G's stand for D, all I's for O and so on.

Now let's start off on an easy one. The statement below in cryptogram code will tell you a fact about cryptograms. Decode the statement in the lines underneath. Since this is your first one, we will give you some hints to start you off.

Here they are: H=C, L=G, W=R, Z=U, X=S, P=K, D=Y, G=B, F=A.

Now here's the cryptogram

NK DTZ YFPJ YMJ YNRJ

—— ——— ———— ——— ————

FSI YWTZGQJ YT IT

——————————————————

YMJR, HWDUYTLWFRX

———————, ——————————

FWJ KZS!

—————————!

After you've solved this one, turn the page for a longer one.

Space-Age Nursery Rhyme

Here's a cryptogram of an old nursery rhyme. It has a Space-Age surprise in it that is not in the original. Solve the cryptogram and you'll see what we mean.

Here's some hints: U=I, P=D, X=L, V=J.

TQK, PUPPXQ, PUPPXQ,
___, _____, _____,

FTQ OMF MZP FTQ
___ ___ ___ ___

RUPPXQ, FTQ OAI
_____, ___ ___

VGYBQP AHQD FTQ
_____ ____ ___

YAAZ, FTQ MEFDAZMGF
____ ___ _____

XMGSTQP FA EQQ EGOT
_____ __ ___ ____

EBADF, MZP FTQ PUET
_____ ___ ___ ____

DMZ MIMK IUFT FTQ
___ ____ ____ ___

EBAAZ.
_____

Seeing Stars

Bugs Meany is selling copies of a photograph that he says was taken by a famous astronomer. It shows the moon and stars, and the astronomer has personally autographed each one. When Encyclopedia Brown sees the photo, however, he tells everyone that it's a fake and no astronomer ever took that picture. How did he know? Here is the photo.

Encyclopedia Brown Word Maze

In this word maze you must find words by drawing a continuous line from letter to letter until you spell the word. For example, we have found the word TIGER for you. You can go forward, backward, up, down, horizontally, vertically and diagonally. However, you cannot jump over any letter. Starting anywhere you want to, find: EN-CYCLOPEDIA, BUGS MEANY (one word in the maze), IDAVILLE, SALLY KIMBALL (one word), CHIEF BROWN (one word).

E	N	B	G	M	E	D	I
Y	C	U	S	A	N	A	L
P	C	L	I	T	Y	V	L
E	O	R	E	G	L	I	A
C	D	I	A	L	E	B	M
H	I	O	W	N	L	Y	I
E	F	B	R	S	A	L	K

Indian Word Find

In *The Case of the Bitter Drink*, the Daughters of the Pioneers hold Indian trials. One of the tests is to drink something really bitter and not make a face. One of the Braves, however, cheats by freezing his mouth, but Encyclopedia finds him out in the end.

Now in the word find below, there are hidden words relating to Indians. You can go forward, backward, vertically, horizontally and diagonally. Draw a pencil line around each word as you find it. Look for: WAMPUM, WARPATH, TOMAHAWK, MOCCASIN, TOMTOM, FEATHER, ARROW, DRUM, BUFFALO, BRAVES and TEPEE.

```
O L A F U B T O N U R D
F E A T H E A R R O A A
O W A M P U M R W K M V
M H R E A E A T W S O A
N T T E P E E A O E C R
U A F E A T H E R V C B
R P T R R A R A R A A E
D R U M M O V O A R S T
R A D O L A F F U B I A
A W T O M T O M O T N P
W A N R U M O W O M E R
B R A V E T O M T O N A
M A C C A S I N O T A W
```

42

Be a Police Artist

Below you will find a witness's description of a man seen robbing a house. See if you can help Encyclopedia Brown get a picture of the suspect. Here is what to do: Read the description and draw in the missing parts. When you have finished, turn to the answer section to see how close your picture comes to the real person.

Here is the description:

"He had dark, curly hair and wore eyeglasses. He also had a large nose and a small mustache. His chin was square."

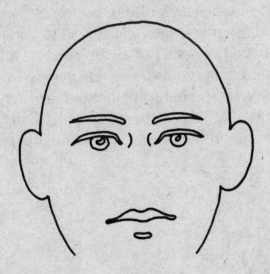

Spot the Clue

This incident happened when Encyclopedia and his father, Chief Brown, were vacationing on a ranch out West. It seemed that the ranch boss had sent a payroll messenger out to the cowboys on the range. It was payday and he was carrying nearly a thousand dollars. A short while later, however, the messenger, who was a tall, thin cowboy, came riding back to the ranch. He was on a different horse. He shouted that he had been robbed. The ranch boss asked what had happened. The cowboy messenger told him that he had been held up by a big cowboy, even taller than he was. The bandit had then made him change horses because the messenger's horse was faster. So the messenger was forced to come back on the bandit's horse. But as the cowboy told his story, still sitting on his horse, Encyclopedia noticed something. That something made Encyclopedia sure that the cowboy was lying. Can you spot the clue in the picture on the next page?

Name Game

Fill in the names going across in the grid below by following the clues. When you're finished, find Encyclopedia Brown's real first name hiding somewhere in the grid. Circle it with a pencil when you do.

ACROSS

1. First name of Brown's junior partner (girl)
2. Girl's name associated with Christmas
3. Boy's name. Rhymes with ferry
4. Last name of the leader of the Tigers
5. Informal form of Louis

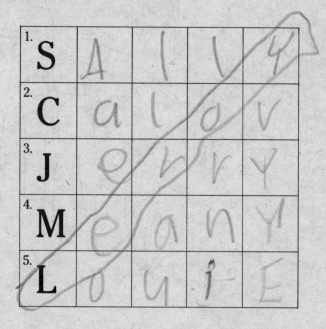

1. S	A	L	L	Y
2. C	a	l	o	v
3. J	e	r	r	Y
4. M	e	a	n	Y
5. L	o	u	i	E

46

Treasure Island

Tubby Jones ran up to Encyclopedia Brown's garage one summer morning all out of breath. "I'm going to be rich!" he yelled, waving a map. He showed Encyclopedia Brown an old treasure map he had found on the beach. It had instructions on where treasure could be found on Gull Island, right off the coast. Encyclopedia studied the map and then said: "Save your breath, Tubby, this map's a fake." How did Encyclopedia know?

Here is a picture of the map.

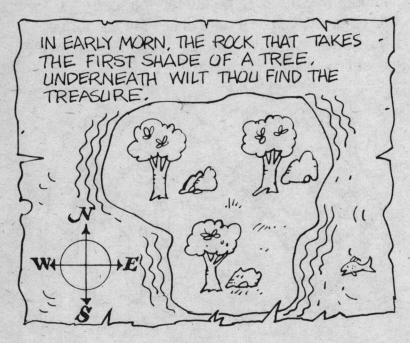

IN EARLY MORN, THE ROCK THAT TAKES THE FIRST SHADE OF A TREE, UNDERNEATH WILT THOU FIND THE TREASURE.

Trapped!

Encyclopedia and his friends are lost in Carson's Caverns. They took a wrong turn somewhere. Now they don't know which way is out and to top it off, they haven't even seen anything yet. But Encyclopedia saves the day. Not only does he lead the gang out but they manage to see every cavern along the way.
Think you can do it?

Here's what to do:

Take a pencil and start at Cavern A. Draw a continuous line through the tunnels that passes through each cavern only once. You cannot visit the same cavern twice and you cannot cross your own line. You must end up at exit E.

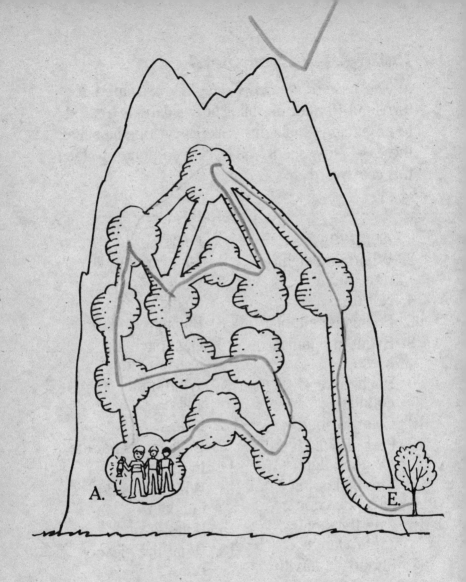

A.

E.

Bullfighter Crossword

In *The Case of the Boy Bullfighter*, a trained dog turns out to a lot of bull. But the gang is treated to an exciting bullfight while Encyclopedia solves the case. Now see if you're brave enough to face this crossword.

ACROSS

2. What a bullfighter must be!
4. Not on
6. Bullfighter's tool
8. Event in Spanish arena
9. Bullfighting country
10. Color for bull
12. Part of bull given for good fight
14. The bull going after the cape
16. One-third of Santa's laugh
17. Reduce in length
20. A bull will do this before he charges
21. Bullring cheer
22. Not strong

DOWN

1. Mexican bandit
2. Places for bullfights
3. Bullfight stadium
5. High-pitched instrument
6. What a bull will do
7. Near
9. Bullfighters parade
11. In
13. What it will do in Spain
15. Bull's weapons
18. What the picador rides
19. Slow, easy run

Spot the Clue

Melvin Moore came running up to Encyclopedia Brown for help. Jack Evinrode had been stealing his gas again! Encyclopedia asked him to explain. Melvin said that Jack Evinrode had a small boat with an outboard motor in the back. He said that he had suspected Jack of stealing gasoline from his boathouse for a while now. He knew that Jack was always spending money on other things so he never had enough to buy gas with. Now it seems that Melvin had actually seen him stealing gasoline that morning. It was now late afternoon. Encyclopedia went down to the dock with Melvin to look for Jack. Just as they got there, they saw Jack tying up his boat. They went over and Melvin demanded that Jack pay for the gas he stole. Jack denied stealing any gas from Melvin and said that as a matter of fact, he had very little gas in his motor.

"That's because you used it all up!" shouted Melvin. Jack said that it wasn't true. He said that, in fact, he had been rowing all day because he had so little gas. He showed Melvin and Encyclopedia two long oars. It was then that Encyclopedia noticed something that tripped Jack up. Can you spot the clue in the picture on the next page?

From Boats to Oats

Encyclopedia loves boating and horseback riding, so it's no surprise that he loves this word game.

Here's what to do:

Just change one letter in each word below that relates to boating so that each word becomes a new word that relates to horses.

PADDLE — _____

SPAR   — _____

MATE   — _____

BOAT   — _____

SAIL   — _____

Answers

Crime Wave, page 7

The four crimes are:
1. Car going the wrong way on a one-way street
2. Boy throwing litter on the sidewalk
3. Same boy crossing street when light says DON'T WALK
4. Posters up on wall that says POST NO BILLS

P. S. If you thought that the van was parked illegally at the
NO PARKING sign, remember it says 10 <u>PM.</u>

The Line-Up, pages 8 & 9

Spider Spinoza is "B." If you didn't get it, read the report again
and you'll see that all the others are eliminated for one reason
or another. For example, the bald man wouldn't have bought
a comb, and so on.

Match the Prints, page 10

Numbers 2 and 8 are exactly alike

Encyclopedia meets The Brain, page 11

The message reads:
I <u>UNDERS</u>TAND THAT YOU NEVER <u>OVER</u>LOOK A CLUE.
IF YOU CAN <u>UNDERS</u>TAND THIS MESSAGE, I WILL
BELIEVE THAT AND ADMIT YOU ARE SMARTER
THAN I AM.

Answers

Prehistoric Word Find, page 12

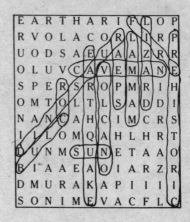

Clue Code, page 13

The message reads: MEET
ME
IN
THE
OLD
BARN
TONIGHT

Sea Monster, page 14

OCTOPUS

Answers

Short-Cut Maze, page 15

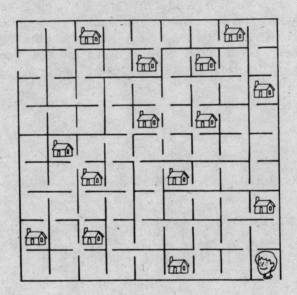

Spot the Clue, pages 16 & 17

Encyclopedia saw that the brick was *outside* the window. If the brick had been thrown through the window from the outside, as the clerk stated, it would have been *inside* the store. Remember, the clerk said that he left everything exactly the way it was.

When caught in his lie, the clerk confessed that he threw the brick from inside the store. He then stole the jewelry himself and made up the story about the thief and the dropped cap.

Answers

Bugs Bugs Brown, pages 18 & 19

Lucy could not *run down the stairs* because, as was stated at the beginning of the story, she lived in a one-level house.

If Mario set his alarm to go off at 9:30 at 9:00 that night, the alarm would go off in a half hour from then. The clock doesn't know PM from AM of course. Since it was said that the *alarm* always woke him up, it means that he woke up a half hour later, or 9:30 PM. Therefore the sun couldn't have been shining.

Name the Case, pages 20 & 21

1. TIGER, 2. THIN, 3. FOE, 4. HMS, 5. SIGN, 6. CASE

T	H	E	C	A	S	E	O	F	T	H	E
M	I	S	S	I	N	G	R	I	N	G	■

The Case of the Busy Chief, page 22

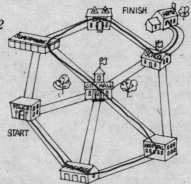

What's in a Name?, page 23

1. Spider, 2. Monkeys, 3. Bird, 4. Bat, 5. Snake, 6. Snail

Answers

Movie Crossword, pages 24 & 25

Pinball Wizard, pages 26 & 27

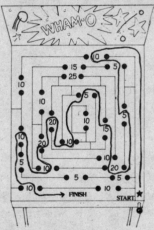

The Two-Bit Mystery, page 28

First move: Turn over the first and second coins.
Second move: Turn over the first and third coins.
Third move: Turn over the first and second coins.

Letter-Wise, page 29

S. The letters stand for the days of the week.
E. The letters stand for: ONE, TWO, THREE, FOUR, and so on.

Answers

Crazy Graffiti, pages 30 & 31

1. Rainfall 2. Lower class 4. Footsteps 5. Hot Dog
6. Flying high 7. Sunrise 8. Half moon 9. Mountain top
10. Longfellow 11. Loose change 12 High brow
13. Double-cross 14. Cut-rate 15. Long shot
16. Short-tempered 17. Tightrope 18. Toss-up

Spider Maze, page 32

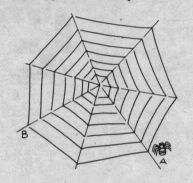

A Visual Trick, page 33

The message reads: HERE IS THE MESSAGE

A Short Mystery, page 34

He stood on a big block of ice that was in the room.
The puddle of water was from the ice when it melted.

Witness to the Crime!, pages 35 & 36

1. 2, 2. 3592, 3. Three O'clock, 4. Idaville First National Bank.
5. Holly Ave. & 4th St, 6. A. Yes, B. Yes, C. Striped,
D. No, E. Yes, 7. 960 Holly Ave.

Answers

Cryptograms, pages 37, 38 & 39

IF YOU TAKE THE TIME
AND TROUBLE TO DO
THEM, CRYPTOGRAMS
ARE FUN!

HEY, DIDDLE, DIDDLE,
THE CAT AND THE
FIDDLE, THE COW
JUMPED OVER THE
MOON, THE ASTRONAUT
LAUGHED TO SEE SUCH
SPORT, AND THE DISH
RAN AWAY WITH THE
SPOON.

Seeing Stars, page 40

The stars could never be seen inside the moon's crescent as shown. The moon would cover them since that part is solid but just in shadow.

Encyclopedia Brown Word Maze, page 41

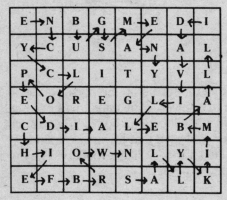

Answers

Indian Word Find, page 42

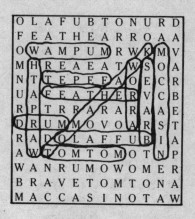

Be a Police Artist, page 43

Spot the Clue, pages 44 & 45

Encyclopedia noticed that the stirrup on the horse was short.
Too short even for the messenger. If the bandit was even taller,
then it couldn't have been a tall bandit's horse. When caught
in his lie, the messenger confessed that he and his friend,
Shorty Smith, had planned it to look like a robbery. They were
to meet later and divide the money.

Answers

Name Game, page 46

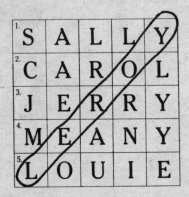

Treasure Island, page 47

By looking at the compass points on the map, Encyclopedia noticed that all the trees were WEST of the rocks. Since the sun rises in the East, in *EARLY MORN* the shadows of the trees would all be facing away from the rocks in the opposite direction. Therefore none of the rocks could *TAKE THE FIRST SHADE OF A TREE.*

Trapped!, pages 48 & 49

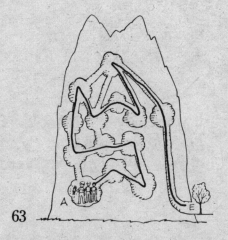

Answers

Bullfighter Crossword, pages 50 & 51

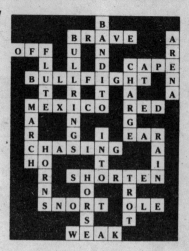

Spot the Clue, pages 52 & 53

Encyclopedia noticed that Jack's boat had no oarlocks. It's practically impossible to row a boat without oarlocks, much less row it around all day. When caught in his lie, Jack confessed to stealing the gas.

From Boats to Oats, page 54

Saddle, Spur, Mare, Boot, Tail

If you enjoyed this book, look for the other *Encyclopedia Brown's Puzzles and Games* books at your favorite bookstore.